3

,9♂

D0982870

THE KING PENGUIN BOOKS

41

BRITISH BUTTERFLIES

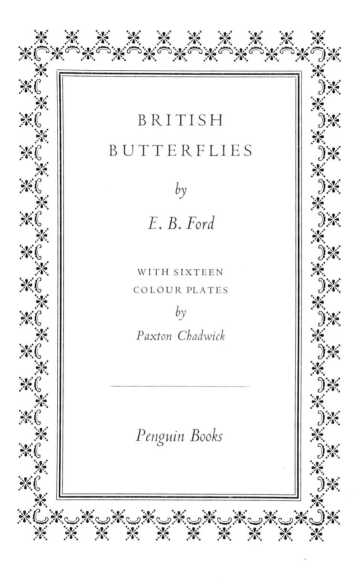

BRITISH BUTTERFLIES

by

E. B. Ford

WITH SIXTEEN
COLOUR PLATES
by
Paxton Chadwick

Penguin Books

THE KING PENGUIN BOOKS

Editor: N. B. L. Pevsner
Technical Editor: R. B. Fishenden

Published by Penguin Books Ltd
Harmondsworth, Middlesex, England
Penguin Books Inc, 3300 Clipper Mill Road
Baltimore, Md, U.S.A., and
Penguin Books Pty Ltd, 200 Normanby Road
Melbourne, Australia

This volume published 1951
Made in Great Britain

Text printed by R. & R. Clark Ltd, Edinburgh
Plates made and printed by
John Swain & Son Ltd, Barnet
Cover designed by Paxton Chadwick

British Butterflies

ALL the smaller books on British butterflies are guides to the identification of the species, with some account of their life-histories, habits, and distribution. The form of presentation may vary, but the ground covered has remained substantially the same. My aim is quite different. I propose briefly and in an elementary way to discuss some of the interesting problems which these insects present. The usual descriptions of the early and adult stages are omitted, for they can easily be found elsewhere, but the information given here has never before been made available in a small compass; I hope it may increase the pleasure by widening the outlook of those who love the countryside. Furthermore, a few statements likely to arouse the curiosity of specialists in other fields are also included. There are, for example, thousands of chemists and mathematicians in Britain: a hint that the study of butterflies has something to offer them does no harm to those whose approach is that of the countryman or the artist. On the contrary, I believe that to the average man it is stimulating to find that the familiar objects of the wayside have unexpected properties of interest in spheres far removed from his own. Further information on the subjects discussed here may be obtained from the works listed in the short Bibliography on p. 31. This also includes references to a few of the standard text-books giving descriptive accounts of each species.

The plates are of course adjusted to the needs of the text. That is to say, they illustrate principles rather than specific differences, and no attempt has been made to figure all the British butterflies yet again. However, the examples are a representative selection, since they are drawn from every one of the classes into which the group is divided.

The chief thing to notice and remember about butterflies is that they are insects, whose fundamental qualities, with their advantages and drawbacks, they share. It is worth while to consider briefly how this fact affects them.

Unlike ourselves, all insects have a hard external skeleton, horny in structure, within which the soft parts, the muscles, nerves and internal organs, are enclosed as within a box. Consequently, they cannot grow continuously as in youth we do, but in a number of distinct stages. The old inelastic cuticle is from time to time sloughed off, and growth then takes place before the new soft one, which has formed below, hardens: a short period, and necessarily so in order to minimize the risk of injury. This is particularly dangerous to insects since their blood does not flow in tubes, or 'blood vessels', as in most animals, but fills all the interstices of the body. With such an arrangement, haemorrhage from a cut or abrasion is usually fatal.

The horny cuticle of 'chitin', though continuous over the surface of an insect, hardens in a series of broad rings, the *segments*, which are generally movable one over another since the connections between them remain soft and pliable. These delicate regions are narrow, and they are usually overlapped by the segment in front, for protection. Such a method of organization is a convenient one, since each segment acts to some extent as a working unit, having, typically, a nerve supply and respiratory system of its own. The pairs of legs and wings are each formed from a single segment only.

The respiration of insects is effected by minute tubes. These open in pairs down the sides of the body and branch internally, becoming less than one-thousandth of a millimetre * in diameter near their ends. They ramify through the tissues and carry to them a direct supply of oxygen, a process in which the blood takes no part. The gas passes along them by diffusion which, in tubes so small, is fast enough for the creature's needs only over a distance of about half an inch. Thus it comes about that no insect has a body much more than one inch in thickness. A few British moths, but none of our butterflies, approach this limit.

The eyes of insects are incapable of focussing, and the curved surface of each is divided into flat *facets*. These are the distal ends of optically separate structures working independently of one another, and in a butterfly about 6000 of them compose each 'compound eye', of which there is a pair. The picture they provide is but an imperfect one, built up from the average value of light falling on every facet. Thus it is formed by a mosaic of separate dots differing in intensity, like that printed in an illustrated newspaper. Naturally its definition depends on the number of facets engaged in perceiving it. This rapidly decreases as the object observed moves further away; to be precise it varies inversely with the square of the distance, so that most insects, including butterflies, are very short-sighted; indeed, when more than about four feet apart one butterfly cannot recognize another as belonging to its own species. On the other hand, such a mechanism is particularly well adapted to detecting movements, which will affect different facets in succession. Evidently the habits of a creature possessed of such eyes must be greatly influenced by their curious structure.

The body of every insect is divided into a head, chest (thorax), and abdomen. The head carries, in addition to the eyes, a pair of jointed rods, the antennae, which are scent-perceiving organs in which the sense of touch is also highly developed. The mouth-

* One millimetre is about twice the thickness of one's thumb-nail.

parts differ greatly from one group to another. They are attached below the head, and in butterflies combine to form a tube, often longer than the body, up which liquids are sucked. When not in use this is coiled like a watch-spring, and is then almost out of sight. The thorax is composed of three segments, each with a pair of legs, and to the second and third are attached the fore and hind wings. The abdomen in butterflies includes ten segments, some of those at the end being modified for genital purposes. It is usually provided with legs in immature insects, but never in the adults. The presence of large ovaries makes the body stouter in the females than in the males.

The two sexes may be superficially similar, as in the Painted Lady (Plate 10), or they may be remarkably distinct (see Plate 11). Very rarely, male and female characteristics are combined in the same individual, as in the Brimstone illustrated on Plate 3, which is butter-yellow in the male and greenish-white in the female.

Butterflies and moths constitute a distinct group of insects, the Order Lepidoptera, whose nearest relatives are the caddis flies. Their most striking feature is the presence of minute coloured scales upon the wings and body, to which their varied hues are due. These are too small to be separately visible to the naked eye, but they come off when the creature is handled and stick to the fingers like dust. When magnified, the majority of those on the wings are seen to be flattened and attached by short stalks, and to overlap one another like slates on a roof. On the body they are more hair-like, as also are some of those on the wings.

Butterflies can be distinguished from moths in a number of ways which are infallible when taken together though each of them is subject to exceptions. The antennae of butterflies always end in a knob, or at least a swelling, while those of moths rarely do so. Butterflies usually rest with their wings raised above the back; moths too may do this, but more often they hold them outspread or wrapped round the body. Butterflies are diurnal while moths may be found upon the wing at all hours, though the majority fly by night. In most but not all moths, the wings on either side are united during flight by a coupling apparatus consisting of bristles from the hind wing which fit into a pocket below the fore wing. This arrangement is absent from butterflies, but a lobe at the base of the hind wings overlaps those in front and serves the same purpose.

Both butterflies and moths pass through four phases during their lives. They reproduce by means of eggs (ova). Each is the size of the head of a pin or even smaller, and they have characteristic shapes and ornamentation in the various species, the surface often being sculptured into complex patterns (p. 11, *a–d*).

A single female normally lays between one hundred and three hundred eggs, and these hatch into caterpillars (larvae). There are many forms of them, some being worm-like, others woodlouse shaped, while they may be beset with branching spines or nearly naked and covered only with a short down (p. 11, *e–g*). Some of the abdominal segments bear legs, which have disappeared in the adult; in structure they are quite different from the three pairs of the thorax, which persist. The compound eyes of the perfect insect have not yet developed, and though the head is indeed provided with several eyes of simple construction the creature is nearly blind.

The caterpillars of butterflies moult four times, at each of which they may undergo a considerable transformation in shape and colour. Finally they moult again to produce the inert chrysalis (pupa), in which the general shape of the adult is foreshadowed: the wings and antennae can be seen, enclosed like the rest of the external organs in hard cases sealed down to the surface. There are three principal types of these chrysalids, each subject to modifications. They may be attached to some object by the tail and held more or less upright by a silken girth; they may be attached by the tail alone and hang head downwards

(p. 11, *h–j*); or, rarely, they may be enclosed in a case, or cocoon, made usually of grass bound together with silk.

After about three weeks, unless the chrysalis remains dormant throughout the winter, the hard case cracks and bursts, and the adult butterfly (imago) crawls out. The wings are at first soft and crumpled and about one-quarter of their proper size, but blood is pumped into them to expand them, and in a few hours they harden and are fit for use.

The relative lengths of these four phases of life vary greatly, that in which winter is passed being, of course, exceptionally prolonged. In some species the cycle occupies the whole year, but in others there may be two or three generations during the summer.

It would be almost impossible to study animals if they were treated merely as a chaotic mixture of forms. For convenience they must inevitably be classified into groups on some logical system, and that adopted is based upon relationship. Thus all the members of a group are more closely related to each other by descent than they are to any other living creatures. A species is a group of animals so much akin that they can interbreed and produce fully fertile offspring. The British butterflies comprise between sixty and seventy such species, but not all are permanent residents in this country.

Those species most nearly allied are included together in an assemblage called a *genus*. Most butterflies are named in two distinct ways, colloquially and scientifically. The colloquial names differ from one language and country to another, but the scientific are international. The colloquial names are arbitrarily bestowed; the scientific are less arbitrary, for all the species in a genus are given a first name in common, with a second (specific) name distinguishing them. Thus three well-known British butterflies are the Red Admiral, *Vanessa atalanta*, the Peacock, *Nymphalis io*, and the Large Tortoiseshell, *Nymphalis polychloros*.

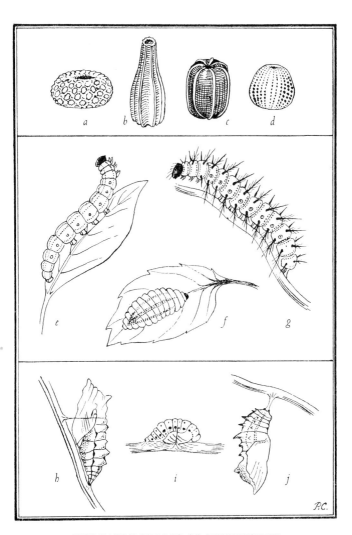

THE EARLY STAGES OF BUTTERFLIES

The scientific names show that the latter are included in the same genus and are thus more closely related to each other than either is to the Red Admiral; a fact which the colloquial or English names do not suggest, or even suggest erroneously, for the Large Tortoiseshell is more closely related to the Peacock than to the Small Tortoiseshell, *Aglais urticae.*

Here we may omit all the larger groupings of classification which intervene between the genus and the principal one dividing British butterflies into eight great families. These families are so distinct that a brief description of each is essential if the range of form and diversity among the species is to be appreciated. They are arranged in an order which on the whole passes from the more specialized down to those which are less sharply distinguished from moths.

Examples of every one of the families are illustrated in colour in this book. To save space, the references in the following summary are to the plates only. The relevant figures on each plate can be obtained from the list on p. 32 in which both names and families are given.

FAMILY DANAIDAE. Large, chiefly tropical, species of slow flight but protected by a disagreeable smell or taste. The front pair of legs is in the perfect insect degenerate and useless for walking. The caterpillars are smooth and the chrysalis hangs head downwards. One species occasionally reaches Britain (Plate 9).

FAMILY SATYRIDAE (the 'Browns'). The members of this group bear eye-like spots upon the wings (Plates 6 and 15). They are predominantly brown or blackish insects, but one of our species is extensively marked with white. This is the Marbled White, *Melanargia galathea* (Plate 1). The front pair of legs is imperfectly developed. The eggs are spherical (p. 11, *d*). The caterpillars are smooth and feed on grass, and the chrysalis hangs head downward or lies in a cocoon.

FAMILY NYMPHALIDAE. These are among the most powerful and conspicuous of butterflies, and include such well-known forms as the Red Admiral, Tortoiseshells, and their allies (Plates 2, 7, 10); also the Fritillaries, which are brownish with black markings and often bear spots or washes resembling metallic silver on the underside (Plates 3, 4, 7, 13). The Purple Emperor, *Apatura iris* (Plate 12), also belongs here. The front pair of legs is degenerate and useless. The eggs are rather flattened, the caterpillars nearly always spined, and the chrysalis is suspended head downwards by the tail alone (p. 11, *c*, *g*, *j*).

FAMILY RIODINIDAE. This is chiefly a South American family, where a great number of species is known, many being brilliantly coloured. Only one reaches Europe, and its range extends to southern England (Plate 13). The front pair of legs is degenerate in the males, fully formed and used for walking in the females. The eggs are spherical, the caterpillars woodlouse shaped, much resembling those of the next family; the chrysalids are rather plump and attached to plants by the tail and a silken girth.

FAMILY LYCAENIDAE. Three somewhat distinct groups are included here, the Blues (Plates 4 and 11), Coppers (Plate 16), and Hairstreaks (Plate 14). Together they form an immense assemblage abundant throughout the world. They are among the smallest of butterflies, that shown on Plate 16 being one of the larger species, and they are to be distinguished from the Riodinidae mainly by the condition of the front legs, which are functional in both sexes. The eggs are disc-like, often elaborately sculptured. Many of the caterpillars are equipped with a honey-gland producing a sweet secretion attractive to ants, which associate with them and act as a guard against the attacks of other insects. The caterpillars of the Lycaenidae are rather similar to those of the Riodinidae, being woodlouse shaped. The chrysalids too are stout and rounded, as in that family (p. 11, *a*, *f*, *i*). Typically they are attached by the tail and a girth of silk round the body, although some have lost these methods of fixation and lie loose among the herbage.

FAMILY PAPILIONIDAE ('Swallow-tails'). Here belong the largest butterflies in the world. The hind wings are usually tailed (Plate 8), and the adult insects use all three pairs of legs for walking. The eggs are spherical. The caterpillars are of varied forms but more or less cylindrical, not woodlouse shaped. Concealed in a pouch behind the head they have a short forked rod which is flashed out and withdrawn like the tongue of a snake when the creature is alarmed. It produces a strong and supposedly protective scent. The chrysalids are angular, supported by the tail and a silken girth (p. 11, *h*).

FAMILY PIERIDAE. Three groups inhabit Britain: the 'Whites' (Plates 1 and 16), including the ordinary 'Cabbage Whites', the 'Yellows' (Plates 3 and 5), and one very exceptional species, the Wood White, *Leptidea sinapis* (Plate 14). All three pairs of legs are fully developed in the adults of this family. The eggs are quite unlike those of other butterflies, being tall and bottle-shaped (p. 11, *b*). The caterpillars are cylindrical and without spines (p. 11, *e*); the chrysalids, which are angular, are supported by the tail and a silken girth.

FAMILY HESPERIIDAE (the 'Skippers'). For reasons which cannot be discussed here, this family should probably be regarded as a group distinct from all other butterflies and somewhat intermediate between them and certain moths; indeed some species do not sit with the wings upright in the butterfly fashion. They are small dull-coloured insects (Plate 11) with a swift darting flight, and the legs of the adults are all functional. The caterpillars are smooth, rather tapering at the ends, and the chrysalids are enclosed in cocoons of grass and silk.

Most of the principal distinctions between these eight families have had to be omitted from this brief account: for instance, the arrangement of the struts, or 'nervures', which strengthen the wings. As already indicated, the Hesperiidae stand alone, but even the few points which have been mentioned will suggest that the other seven fall into two main divisions, that is to say, those (the Danaidae, Satyridae, and Nymphalidae) with the first pair of legs degenerate in the adult stage and the chrysalis hanging head downwards attached only by the tail, and those (the Lycaenidae, Papilionidae, and Pieridae) in which all three pairs of walking legs are functional in the butterfly state and in which the chrysalis is held in a more or less upright position by a silken girdle (probably the last remnant of a complete case or cocoon). The Riodinidae help to bridge the gap between these two groups.

It is a difficult matter to make the classification of animals reflect relationship, and it may be questioned if the attempt is reasonably successful. Conceivably some of the features thought to indicate affinity do not, being independently acquired in different species; if so, a grouping based upon them would be artificial, and its supposed bearing upon genealogy an illusion. Various safeguards designed to avoid errors of that kind are in use, and we have strong reasons for thinking that on the whole they work well, but any independent evidence of their efficiency is much to be desired. In butterflies and moths, this has lately been obtained by the application of chemical methods.

The varied colours of these insects are produced in two distinct ways. They are sometimes structural, and caused by diffraction from the surface, as are those on a soap bubble. More usually, however, they are due to pigments enclosed within the scales. The chemistry of these substances was not taken into account in classification, being unknown until recently, nevertheless it is clearly associated with the accepted arrangement, which it therefore confirms on independent grounds. Two of the tests employed are so instructive that they may appropriately be mentioned here.

The white colouring matter of the Cabbage Whites and their allies (the Pieridae) is leucopterin, a substance built up from uric acid, which is an excretory product of butterflies as it is of men. The bright yellow colours of that group (for example, those of the Brimstone, *Gonepteryx rhamni*, Plate 3, and of the Clouded Yellow, *Colias croceus*, Plate 5) are due to xanthopterin, a slightly less oxidized form of the same substance. So far as is known, these uric acid pigments occur in every species of this family but not outside it. I have lately shown that they can be recognized in a simple way. If the insect is exposed to chlorine for twenty minutes and is then fumed with ammonia,* the white is changed in a few hours to a beautiful purple. One of the three Small Whites, *Pieris rapae*, shown on Plate 1, has been so treated. It is the first time that the effect has been illustrated. The corresponding yellow pigment (xanthopterin) is immediately converted to the white by chlorine, and then behaves in the same manner. This reaction is a decisive and sensitive test for these substances.

The uric acid pigments contain nitrogen, but the white and yellow colouring matter of flowers, present also in the leaves of many plants, does not. This is generally due to flavones: substances never manufactured by animals, though a few make use of those they obtain from their food. The species that do so are chiefly butterflies and include seven genera of the Satyridae, two of which are British: a member of one of them, the Marbled White, *Melanargia galathea*, is shown on Plate 1. The white markings of this insect therefore do not turn purple on exposure to chlorine; on the other hand, they change to a deep yellow when, without any previous treatment, they are fumed with ammonia. This reaction is characteristic of flavone pigments and is capable of detecting minute traces of them; in butterflies, the

* This reaction is also obtained, more slowly but more brilliantly, if the specimen is not exposed to ammonia after treatment with chlorine.

yellow colour so produced soon disappears. The effect is striking and is known to many naturalists, though they may not always realize its significance.

Flavones can also be demonstrated in the Wood White, *Leptidea sinapis* (Plate 14). Their quantity is small, but the reaction on fuming a fresh specimen with ammonia is unmistakable. Now this is a matter of interest, since the Wood White is a most exceptional butterfly. Its structure is that of a strange isolated group (the sub-family Dismorphiinae), almost entirely restricted to Central and South America: rather a surprising conclusion. Yet this is the only section of the family in which flavone pigments occur, so that the unexpected affinities of the Wood White have been corroborated on chemical grounds unknown when they were originally determined. Being a member of the Pieridae, this species also possesses uric acid pigments, as can easily be shown by exposing a specimen to chlorine.

These two tests are so easily carried out that any amateur naturalist could apply them and perhaps extend our information on the distribution of the substances they so clearly demonstrate. This is already well known in British butterflies, but not in the moths, on which preliminary tests only have so far been carried out. They have disclosed flavones in a few foreign species, but so far no uric acid pigments, though these may not be limited to the pierine butterflies as they at present seem to be. Such simple studies would be a useful contribution to knowledge.

Some species are markedly constant in appearance, while others are highly variable, a fact which has always aroused the interest of naturalists and collectors. Indeed it is hardly possible to study any group of animals, certainly not the butterflies, without being led to enquire at least superficially into the causes and effects of their variability.

At the outset, it may obviously be produced by environmental changes, for the *seasonal variation* of insects is well known. Many butterflies have more than one generation in the year, and the summer brood may differ in a characteristic way from that of the spring or autumn.

For example, the Comma Butterfly, *Polygonia c-album*, begins to hatch from the chrysalis in early July. The first specimens to appear have a yellowish-brown underside bearing in shining white a mark shaped like the letter C (Plate 2, Figs. *a* and *b*). They mate at once and give rise to a generation which develops quickly, producing butterflies in mid-September. These differ from their parents in several ways. They have a charcoal-black underside, on which the white C-like mark remains, the wings are of a more reddish shade above and their edges are even more deeply scalloped (Plate 2, Fig. *c*). However, those specimens of the first brood which emerge later, at the end of July or in early August, are identical with the September butterflies; like them also, but unlike their earlier brothers and sisters, they survive the winter, mating only in the spring. At that season, therefore, individuals of the two broods pair indiscriminately and produce eggs from which the summer generation containing insects of two types, the earlier and the later, is again repeated.

Many other instances illustrating the effect of the environment could be quoted. Thus the common Cabbage Whites have two generations in the year; the spring form being less heavily marked with black than the summer. Moreover, certain species can be made to vary in a striking way by experimental treatment. Thus if chrysalids of the familiar Small Tortoiseshell, *Aglais urticae*, be kept warm, the insects which emerge from them are of a particularly bright reddish colour; while by subjecting them to extreme cold, dark, even smoky, specimens are produced. Similar varieties are encountered from time to time in the open, and are no doubt the product of chrysalids which have been exposed to extremes of temperature. Clearly then the appearance of a butterfly can be influenced by the external conditions in which it lives, changes in which can produce *environmental variation*.

On the other hand, varieties are with about equal frequency of a different origin, being intrinsic as it were; due to the hereditary constitution of the body, like the eye colours of human beings. Now geographical variation is a notable feature of certain species, specimens from different parts of the country being clearly distinguishable (Plates 4 and 6). From what has just been said, it is evident that this may in part be due to environmental effects. We have, however, clear evidence that this is not always or even usually so: the difference between two parts of Britain at the same season being in some important respects much less than that between spring and summer at the same place. Indeed the hereditary nature of such variation can usually be established without question. For if females be obtained from different districts and their progeny reared together under identical conditions, the resulting butterflies generally retain the distinctive characteristics of each race.

Both parents transmit hereditary qualities to their offspring, and they do so to an equal degree. The mechanism which ensures this is responsible also for the intrinsic, or *genetic*, variation of animals and plants which, like the environmental type, may be either 'discontinuous' or 'continuous' in its effects.

Many qualities are inherited in two or more contrasted forms which reappear from generation to generation in definite proportions. This is *discontinuous variation*. For example, there exists a rare variety of the Small Pearl-bordered Fritillary, *Argynnis selene*, in which the ordinary bright, rather reddish brown, ground colour of the wings is replaced by silvery white, the usual black pencillings being retained (Plate 4). If either a male or a female of this type be mated with one of the usual brown shade, all the offspring are brown also. On intercrossing two of them, it is found that the white variety reappears in one-quarter of their progeny, being the inbred grandchildren of the original pair. The points especially to notice are that the capacity to produce the white coloration has been transmitted and that individuals are either of one shade or the other, for intermediates are absent.

Discontinuous variation is of course not restricted to the condition in which one of the alternatives is a great rarity, as in the last instance. On the contrary, all of them may be fairly common, even equally so, and an example of this kind is supplied by the Clouded Yellow, *Colias croceus* (Plate 5). It illustrates also some other curious features, one of which has only just been discovered.

The males of this butterfly always have an orange ground-colour, but the females are of two forms: one, the commoner, is orange like the males, while the other varies from a light primrose shade to white. The proportion of this pale variety, *helice*, fluctuates from about 5 to 15 per cent of the females. A similar situation is found in many closely allied foreign species. The difference in colour is inherited, and that in a simple way, for a pale female transmits to half her offspring the tendency to produce the pale form. Among her daughters it is realized, half being pale and half orange, but among her sons it is not. All of them are orange, though half, those potentially pale as it were, produce pale as well as orange daughters, and in equality. This is *sex-controlled inheritance*, in which a quality is transmitted equally by both sexes but is manifest only in one of them: like early baldness in Man, in which, however, the parts taken by the sexes are reversed, for here it is the female which transmits invisibly.

Dr W. Hovanitz, working on the closely allied *Colias eurytheme* in North America, has recently shown that the corresponding forms of that butterfly differ from one another more profoundly than their colours alone suggest, for the pale females are the more active in the early morning, and perhaps towards evening, while the orange are the more active at other times. This alters the frequencies with which they are to be caught as the day advances. A similar tendency is apparent in their geographical distribution, for the pale females are relatively commoner at high altitudes and in the far north. It is evidently related to the physical features of the environment and is known to be dependent upon both solar radiation and temperature, perhaps also upon relative humidity; but to what extent each of these agencies contributes to the result is still uncertain.

Inherited differences in behaviour must be important in adjusting an animal to the conditions in which it lives. But they are elusive things and difficult to study except when associated with a quality more easily recognized, like the colour-variation of *Colias eurytheme* and, probably, of our own Clouded Yellow, *Colias croceus*, also. Some evidence for the latter suggestion already exists, but it is incomplete; if those interested in British butterflies can confirm it, a valuable field of enquiry awaits them.

Variation is said to be 'continuous' when it does not fall into sharply defined classes but covers a range from one extreme to the other, the intermediates being the commonest. This is the situation with which we are familiar in human height. It is generally due, in an approximately equal degree, to the action of heredity and of the environment. The hereditary aspect of continuous variation makes it possible to shift the average of the population in either direction, and to obtain forms of a more extreme kind, by means of *selection*. That is to say, if rather exceptional individuals are chosen for breeding, their unusual qualities are to some extent transmitted to their offspring, which therefore tend to differ from their parents' generation. The repetition of this process leads to a progressive change. A remarkable illustration of its efficiency is shown on Plate 3. The extent of the black markings on the Marsh Fritillary, *Euphydryas aurinia*, is subject to considerable variation, Figs. *b, d* being rather extreme light and dark forms respectively. It is of the continuous kind, for every degree of intermediacy exists between these examples. Mr J. Shepherd bred this species for ten generations, selecting as parents the darkest specimens of every family, and in the end produced a brood of which the extraordinary butterfly shown in Fig. *e* is typical. This is a blackish insect with a few white spots, and it bears little resemblance to the normal form, of which Fig. *c* is a fair representative.

It is not difficult to see that a corresponding process can occur in nature, since those individuals which are the best fitted for life leave most descendants, and transmit to them some measure of their superior qualities. Here is a mechanism capable of adapting animals to their environments and causing them gradually to change or *evolve*. It can adjust a butterfly to diverse conditions within its range and so subdivide it into local races. These may ultimately diverge from one another so much that they may no longer be able to interbreed and must then be judged distinct species. The process is, however, a slow one, and it generally requires some thousands of generations to produce any recognizable effects. But there is no limit as to their kind; they may, for instance, involve changes in size, colour-pattern, or habits, as the following examples show.

The Mountain Ringlet, *Erebia epiphron*, our one alpine butterfly, reached Britain during the last Ice Age, which ended approximately ten thousand years ago. It has survived since that time on certain mountains, to which it is now confined. One race inhabits the English Lake District, where it rarely descends below 1800 feet; another, found in Perthshire, can tolerate a slightly lower elevation. The chief difference between these two populations is one of size, the English specimens being slightly the smaller (Plate 6).

The Large Heath, *Coenonympha tullia* (Plate 6), is also a relic of the Ice Ages. Though many of its localities are almost at sea level, it does not extend farther south in Britain than Shropshire and North Staffordshire, an area in which it is probably now extinct, and Central Wales, where it yet survives. It is still common in a few places in the North of England and on many of the moors and wastes of Scotland. The specimens from the centre and north of that country (Fig. *b*) are paler and greyer than those from the English Midlands (Fig. *d*) and almost lack their conspicuous eye-like spots. An intergrading series connects these extreme forms and occupies a wide range of country between them, from a considerable part of which, however, the species has unfortunately disappeared during the present century. The Cumberland specimens are approximately intermediate in all respects (Figs. *a* and *c*).

The geographical variation of the Large Heath should be contrasted with that of the Brown Argus, *Aricia agestis* (Plate 4), in which English and Scotch forms also exist. These are, however, distinct and merge with one another only along a relatively narrow belt which passes obliquely from Northumberland to North Lancashire, omitting Cumberland and most of the Lake District. They probably originated in isolation and later extended their range until they met. Thus they would become adjusted to their environments in different ways, so that the intermediates between them are likely to be at a disadvantage, and for this reason they do not spread and produce a gradual transition from one race to the other.

Butterflies, like other animals, experience increasing difficulties towards the edge of their range, where they approach regions in which they cannot survive. These they sometimes overcome by adapting themselves accurately to the special conditions of a few favoured areas. In such places their habits may, in consequence, be quite exceptional. The modifications which evoke such changes in behaviour may or may not affect the appearance of the insects as well.

Thus the Glanville Fritillary, *Melitaea cinxia* (Plate 7), has always been an exceedingly local species in Britain, and is now found only in the Isle of Wight. Even there it rarely strays far inland, though it is abundant on some of the 'undercliffs' and the slopes between the cultivated land and the shore. However, its needs are less exacting elsewhere, for it is not particularly a coastal butterfly on the Continent. Yet English specimens are identical in appearance with those from other countries. So also are English examples of the Large Tortoiseshell, *Nymphalis polychloros* (Plate 7). This insect was at one time widespread over southern England, but became rarer towards the end of last century and has since been able to maintain itself only in the relatively dry East Anglian area.

A contrast is provided by the English race of the Swallow-tail, *Papilio machaon* (Plate 8), which could not be confused with any other. The yellow ground-colour is of a deeper shade than in French specimens, while the dark markings are heavier and one of the bands is of a different shape. In addition, the species has quite distinct habits here: with us it is a marsh insect, being confined to Wicken Fen in Cambridgeshire and to the Norfolk Broads; it feeds only upon the Milk Parsley, *Peucedanum palustre*, and is non-migratory. On the Continent it ascends to considerable altitudes, feeds upon several umbelliferous plants, including cultivated carrots, and wanders extensively over the countryside. Indeed the specimens sometimes caught in the south-east of England, especially Kent, have on examination always proved to be of French origin. They reproduce themselves in favourable seasons, but the stock cannot survive permanently: evidently it is not adapted to the English climate, as is our own race with its peculiar characteristics.

Such migration is partly or wholly responsible for maintaining certain butterflies in Britain. The Large White, *Pieris brassicae*, and the closely related Small White, *P. rapae* (Plate 1), which cause so much damage to cabbages, are both indigenous here; but the stock is augmented in some seasons by vast hordes migrating from the Continent, and it is the excess population so produced which is so destructive. These butterflies have been seen in mid-Channel making for England, and coming in from the sea on the South Coast, as a migrating swarm of such dimensions that the observers thought a bank of low cloud was approaching.

Several other species which successfully maintain themselves here are reinforced by a certain number of immigrants from abroad, but one or two even of our common butterflies are wholly dependent upon arrivals from overseas. These generally reach our shores in the spring and in favourable seasons reproduce themselves and may even become abundant in the summer; however, they are unable to survive an English winter, during which the stock perishes, to be replenished again from the Continent next year. Even such a familiar, and in some seasons common, butterfly as the Painted Lady, *Vanessa cardui* (Plate 10), is of this kind, so is the Clouded Yellow, *Colias croceus* (Plate 5): if migration were to cease, these butterflies would at once become extinct in Britain.

There are others which seldom migrate to this country and on arrival generally fail to reproduce themselves, or do so inadequately, while any descendants which survive die at the approach of winter. These are the rare migrants, such as the Bath White, *Pontia daplidice*, or the Queen of Spain Fritillary, *Argynnis lathonia*, so prized by collectors. Most of them are inhabitants of Central or Southern Europe, but one splendid species, the Camberwell Beauty, *Nymphalis antiopa* (Plate 10), comes to us from Scandinavia. A few individuals arrive in most years, but in this instance always in the autumn, and some certainly hibernate successfully. Yet they do not pair until the spring, when they are probably too widely scattered to find mates even if, as sometimes happens, there has been a small influx of them. But it is probable that other factors, perhaps the damp of our winters, contribute to prevent this fine insect from colonizing Britain. It has indeed been known as a rarity here for over two hundred years and its colloquial name commemorates the capture in August 1748 of two specimens near Camberwell; then a country village, but long since engulfed within modern London.

Some mystery surrounds the occurrence in the British Isles of the great North American Monarch Butterfly, *Danaus plexippus* (Plate 9), which is much the largest species we possess and our only member of the Family Danaidae. Between 150 and 200 specimens have been recorded as seen or captured, while less than a dozen are known from the whole of the rest of Europe. The fact that in its own home it is a great migrant and that it is a large and powerful insect has led to the suggestion that it flies the Atlantic. I cannot believe this myself, even though I have seen a butterfly (the Small White) rest on a calm sea and successfully rise again; nor does the view accord with the fact that none was recorded in this country until 1876, though much interest was taken in butterflies before that time, and so conspicuous an insect would not have escaped attention had it always been reaching us. It is in fact probable that, attracted by the cargo, it takes a passage on fruit boats, which began to sail frequently in the latter part of last century; and indeed specimens have been seen to fly out on opening the hold. Its food-plants, the Milkweeds, *Asclepias*, are not indigenous and are little grown in England, nor has the species a hibernating stage in which it could pass the winter in suspended animation, so it could never become established with us.

It must not be supposed that all butterflies are habitual or even sporadic migrants. Many are restricted to their particular haunts and seldom stray even short distances from them, nor are they known to undertake long journeys. Thus they become closely adapted to certain types of habitat so that downs, woods, and marshes are populated by species characteristic of them. An examination of some of these butterflies captured in different parts of the country and in various years reveals that persistent features, sometimes large, sometimes minute, may distinguish them. These could not have become established in a wandering population.

Plate 11 illustrates a group of three butterflies typical of chalk or limestone downs in the south of England. To such places they are entirely restricted. Two of them, the Chalk-hill Blue, *Lysandra coridon*, and the Adonis Blue, *Lysandra bellargus*, are markedly different in the male sex, the one silvery turquoise above and the other intense azure, but the females are blackish and almost identical. The caterpillars of both feed on Horse-shoe Vetch, *Hippocrepis comosa*, a plant of mainly southern distribution which grows only on an alkaline soil. However, the localization of the third species, the Silver-spotted Skipper, *Hesperia comma*, must be due to factors of a more subtle kind, since its food consists of various common grasses and leguminous plants.

Several typical woodland butterflies are figured on Plates 12, 13, 14. The resplendent Purple Emperor, *Apatura iris* (Plate 12), never a common species, is an inhabitant of certain large oak, and occasionally beech, woods in the south of England, though the caterpillar eats sallow, *Salix caprea*, only. The glancing shades of purple on the wings, changing with the direction of the light, are absent from the female. It is an exceedingly powerful insect, often soaring round the tree-tops and sometimes ascending far above them, though it occasionally comes to earth to drink at a foul puddle or suck the juices from a rotting carcase. The little Purple Hairstreak, *Thecla quercus* (Plate 14), somewhat suggests a diminutive copy of it, being also a butterfly of oak woods. Moreover, the upper surface of the wings is likewise blackish with a sheen of purple; this, however, is present, though differently distributed, in both sexes, while in other respects the markings of the two species are quite dissimilar. Nor are they at all alike in their general structure, for they belong to different families (the Nymphalidae and Lycaenidae respectively). The caterpillars of the Purple Hairstreak feed on oak, and in late June and July the perfect insects fly round these and other trees in many of the woods of England, Scotland except the far north, and central and southern Ireland.

Several of the Fritillaries are forest insects, among them the High Brown, *Argynnis cydippe* (Plate 13). The Duke of Burgundy, *Hamearis lucina* (Plate 13), our one member of the Riodinidae, is also a butterfly of sunny paths and glades, where in May it flies low over the ground, frequently resting on hot bare patches of earth and on leaves, but seldom visiting flowers. It is a localized species, being absent from many places apparently well suited to it even within its range, which is almost restricted to some of the southern English counties though it is also established in a small area in the south of the Lake District. It delights in hot sunshine and its caterpillars feed on cowslips and primroses, so that the reason for this insect's association with woods is not very obvious. Yet it is occasionally to be found also in secluded hollows on downland, so that shelter, such as forest conditions pre-eminently provide, is probably a necessity to it.

The remaining woodland butterfly illustrated here is the Wood White, *Leptidea sinapis* (Plate 14). The contrast which this provides is complete, for it is a true lover of shade. It is especially at home in dense undergrowth and often passes with feeble yet persistent flight from thicket to thicket, usually ignoring any clearings it may cross on the way. It is found in rather widely scattered localities in the southern Midlands and the south of England and, as a distinct geographical race, in a few places in southern Ireland. The peculiar characteristics of this insect, in some ways so unlike other British butterflies, are in harmony with its isolated position as a representative of an exotic group (p. 15).

These and other localized butterflies form colonies which are often in partial or complete isolation from one another. Information on the extent to which minor barriers within their habitats, such as a few fields or a wood unsuited to them, prevent different communities from mixing is at present almost lacking; for the study of such small-scale movements has been neglected, while the occurrence of migration over long distances has attracted much attention, for it is spectacular but in general of far less importance.

Yet it is possible to estimate the interchange between neighbouring populations now it is known that butterflies and moths can be marked satisfactorily with dots of cellulose paint. These dry in about ten seconds and seal the scales on to the wing membrane; they are then permanent and waterproof. Their colour and position can be made to distinguish different colonies. The Meadow Brown, *Maniola jurtina* (Plate 15), inhabits fields, downs of rough grass, and similar places. On the uninhabited island of Tean, Isles of Scilly, where W. H. Dowdeswell and I studied this butterfly, it flies among long grass, bracken, and brambles, but is divided into three populations by two narrow wind-swept necks of land, covered with short turf, which it does not colonize. During a period of eighteen days we marked 1569 specimens so as to indicate, among other things, their area of capture. We recaught 184 of them, but only 3 had crossed to another colony, while one was found in one of the intervening regions. These, though less than 200 yards long, therefore constitute rather effective barriers to the passage of this insect.

The use of this marking technique makes it possible also to determine the number of individuals composing such colonies. Suppose, for example, we catch, mark, and release 100 specimens in an isolated population of butterflies. If, after allowing them to become thoroughly dispersed, we catch another 100 and find that 10 of them are marked, we calculate that the colony consists of $100 \times 100 \div 10 = 1000$ specimens. This is only a first approximation, and much more detailed and accurate methods of making such estimates, depending upon the analysis of repeated samples, have now been devised. The Meadow Brown from Tean illustrated on Plate 15, Fig. *c*, has been marked three times and each dot of paint indicates, by its colour and position, a date of capture.

Moreover, by such means it is possible to determine the average length of life of the individuals, which can therefore be compared in differing conditions and in populations of varying sizes. The results of such work are far-reaching, but only one of them can be mentioned here: it confirms the suggestion that very small populations, of perhaps 500 or less, have an unduly high mortality. Such colonies therefore are maintained only if they receive some augmentation from outside, and any isolated community whose numbers become reduced to this level is in danger of extinction. The Black-veined White, *Aporia crataegi* (Plate 16), was in that condition during the first two decades of this century, for, though a common butterfly in some parts of the Continent, in this country it survived only in two restricted areas in Kent. However, it could not maintain itself even there, and seems finally to have disappeared about 1924.

Now it is a notable fact that the numbers of butterflies, as of other animals, are far from constant. They fluctuate not only in response to good and bad seasons but also over a long cycle of years. Numerous species became rarer or more restricted in range from about 1830 onwards. It was at this time that we lost at least one British species, the Large Copper, *Lycaena dispar*, and our race of it was the finest known. There is good reason to think that the draining of many of the fens in which it lived, and the over-collecting to which it was subjected, were not sufficient to encompass its destruction, but contributed to that result at a time when its numbers were being reduced by long-term climatic agencies. A very similar form of the same species from Holland (Plate 16) was introduced into two localities here about twenty years ago, in one of which, Wood Walton Fen, Huntingdon, it continues to survive, though rather precariously.

The present century has witnessed the other phase of this cycle. Thus many species of British butterflies have gradually become commoner since the first World War. Yet this period has been a disastrous one for the countryside. During it, the great estates, so important for the maintenance of rural life, have been breaking up, suburban and industrial conditions have made hideous extensions, vast areas of woodland have been felled, while afforestation has been too much restricted to the planting of conifers. The apparently favourable reaction of our butterflies to such evils is misleading and made in spite of them. When their numbers are reduced again, as they will be, they will sink lower than ever before, and many colonies and perhaps some further species will be wiped out. Thus any attempt to save them when their time of need comes must depend ultimately upon success in the struggle to save the British countryside: and that battle is probably a losing one.

BIBLIOGRAPHY

The following works provide further information on the subjects discussed here. Original papers are included, since some of the facts mentioned are not yet to be found in books. The scope of these references is briefly indicated; those listed as 'descriptive text-books' may be consulted for descriptions of the species, their times of appearance, and localities.

FISHER, R. A. and FORD, E. B. (1947): *Heredity*, *1*, 143-174 (Methods of estimating population-numbers)

FORD, E. B. (1941): *Proceedings*, *Royal Entomological Society*, A, *16*, 65-90 (Chemical methods of classification)

FORD, E. B. (1946): *Butterflies* (*New Naturalist Series*). London: Collins (General biology of butterflies, includes heredity)

FORD, E. B. (1947): *Proceedings*, *Royal Entomological Society*, A, *22*, 72-76 (Chemical methods of classification)

FROHAWK, F. W. (1934): *The Complete Book of British Butterflies*. London: Ward, Lock (Descriptive text-book)

IMMS, A. D. (1937): *Recent Advances in Entomology*. London: Churchill (Structure and senses of insects)

SOUTH, R. (1941, first published 1906): *The Butterflies of the British Isles*. London: Warne (Descriptive text-book)

a

b

c

d

1. *Butterfly Pigments*

2. *Environmental Variation*

3. *Genetic Variation*

4. *Genetic Variation*

5. *Genetic Variation*

6. *Northern Butterflies*

7. *Localized Butterflies*

8. *A Localized Butterfly*

9. *A Migratory Butterfly*

a

b

10. *Immigrant Species*

11. *Butterflies of Chalk Downs*

12. *A Forest Butterfly*

13. *Woodland Butterflies*

14. *Woodland Butterflies*

15. *A Butterfly of Grass-lands and Meadows*

16. *Extinct and Re-introduced Species*